# How Bear Lost His Tail

adapted by Martin Curtis
illustrated by Wallace Keller

## Harcourt
SCHOOL PUBLISHERS

Printed in the United States of America

ISBN 10: 0-15-350486-2
ISBN 13: 978-0-15-350486-0

Ordering Options
ISBN 10: 0-15-350333-5 (Grade 3 Below-Level Collection)
ISBN 13: 978-0-15-350333-7 (Grade 3 Below-Level Collection)
ISBN 10: 0-15-357470-4 (package of 5)
ISBN 13: 978-0-15-357470-2 (package of 5)

1 2 3 4 5 6 7 8 9 10 179 15 14 13 12 11 10 09 08 07 06

Long ago, many animals looked different.
Take Bear. He had a long tail of thick and
shiny fur.

Bear was proud of his tail. He brushed
it each day. When he went for a walk, he
waved his tail in the air.

"Hello, Duck!" said Bear. "Doesn't my tail look lovely today?"

"I guess so," shrugged Duck.

"Hello, Rabbit!" said Bear. "Look at my tail. Isn't the fur thick? Isn't it shiny?"

"It's fine," replied Rabbit.

"Coyote!" said Bear. "Your little tail is nice, but mine is nicer."

Everyone was tired of Bear's bragging, especially Coyote. He decided it was time to teach Bear a lesson.

"Your tail is beautiful!" exclaimed Coyote. "The fur is thick and shiny. See you later!" Then Coyote ran to the pond.

The pond was covered in ice. Coyote found a place where he knew Bear would see him. He broke a hole in the ice and began to catch fish. He piled the fish around the hole. When he saw Bear, Coyote dropped his tail into the hole in the ice.

Bear saw Coyote and the piles of fish. He felt as hungry as if he were living through a famine. Then he saw that Coyote's tail was hanging in the water. Bear's gaze was filled with curiosity.

"What are you doing?" asked Bear.

"I'm fishing," replied Coyote.

"I've never seen anyone fish like that," said Bear.

"I can teach you," said Coyote.

"That is generous of you!" cried Bear.

"Absolutely," said Coyote, "but we need to find you a new spot where there are plenty of fresh fish."

Bear was agreeable. He watched Coyote break a new hole in the ice. As he worked, Coyote explained that Bear must carefully follow his instructions. That was fine with Bear, who was already thinking about his big fish banquet.

"Now, Bear, sit here next to this hole," said Coyote.

Bear lay down and put his paws in the water as bears do.

"No!" cried Coyote. "Sit this way."

Coyote sat down and turned his back to the hole. Then he placed his tail in the water.

Bear was suspicious. It was a strange
way to fish.

"Why do I have to sit that way?"
asked Bear.

Coyote sighed. "Then the fish can grab
your tail."

"How will I know that a fish is there if
I can't see it?" asked Bear.

"I will wait over there by that tree," said Coyote. "When I see a fish grab your tail, I will yell PULL! Then jump up, and pull your tail out of the water with all your might. The fish will come out of the water with your tail."

Now it made sense to Bear. He turned around and dropped his tail into the water.

Coyote sat next to the tree. He waited until Bear fell asleep. Then Coyote went home to his den.

Coyote returned the next morning. He quietly crept up to sleeping Bear. Then he hollered into Bear's ear.

"PULL!"

Bear jumped. He pulled his tail as hard as he could, but his tail had frozen in the ice overnight. When he pulled, his tail broke off! Bear only had a short stump left.

Coyote laughed. He had pulled off another trick. To this day, all bears have short tails. They also don't like coyotes very much!

# Think Critically

1. What is the main idea of this story?

2. How does Coyote get Bear to put his tail in the water?

3. How would you describe Coyote?

4. Why does Coyote tell Bear that he will wait next to the tree?

5. Do you think Coyote was right to play the trick on Bear? Why or why not?

 **Social Studies**

**All About Bears** There are many kinds of bears that live in the United States. Find out about some of the kinds of bears and the names of the states where they live.

 **School-Home Connection** Retell this story to a family member. Act it out to make it more interesting.

**Word Count:** 560